CENTENNIAL
ROYAL CONSERVATORY
18 86
OF MUSIC · TORONTO

Celebration
SERIES

© *Copyright 1988 by The Frederick Harris Music Co., Limited*
All Rights Reserved

ISBN 0-88797-318-3

FREDERICK
HARRIS
MUSIC

Official Examination Repertoire of the
Royal Conservatory of Music – Grade 1

Répertoire officiel des examens du
Royal Conservatory of Music – Niveau 1

The Centennial Celebration Series of the Royal Conservatory of Music offers teachers, students, and those who play the piano solely for their own enjoyment, a carefully selected and well-balanced collection of compositions of the highest quality. Pianists at all levels of development will find the series to be of exceptional musical and pedagogical value.

This series is the collective product of more than 100 years of teaching and performing experience, and represents countless hours of dedicated effort by compilers and editors from the staff of the Royal Conservatory of Music and The Frederick Harris Music Co., Limited. The repertoire and studies in this series are drawn from official Royal Conservatory of Music examination material as determined by the Royal Conservatory of Music Piano Syllabus. Students and teachers are urged to consult the most recent Syllabus for current examination requirements and procedures.

Editorial markings have been applied conservatively for the convenience of the performer. Students and teachers are encouraged to consider interpretive alternatives in the interest of individually sensitive and imaginative performances. With the exception of *da capo* indications, repeats should be omitted during examinations.

The Royal Conservatory of Music takes pride in its 100 years of service to the international music community and wishes all who use the Centennial Celebration Series the joy of discovery and much musical satisfaction.

La Centennial Celebration Series du Royal Conservatory of Music offre aux professeurs, aux étudiants, et à ceux qui jouent du piano pour leur seul plaisir, une collection de la plus haute qualité, choisie avec soin et bien équilibrée. Pianistes de tout calibre trouveront cette série d'une grande valeur tout autant musicale que pédagogique.

Cette série, la réalisation conjuguée de plus de 100 ans d'expérience collective dans l'enseignement et l'interprétation de la musique, représente des heures incalculables de travail de la part des compilateurs et des éditeurs, membres du personnel du Royal Conservatory of Music et de la Frederick Harris Music Co., Limited. Le répertoire et les études font partie du programme officiel décrit dans le syllabus pour piano du Royal Conservatory of Music. Etudiants et professeurs sont priés de consulter le syllabus le plus récent pour les exigences et les règlements des examens.

Les ajouts d'édition dans ce livre ont été appliqués avec soin pour faciliter l'interprétation de l'exécutant. Dans l'intérêt de la sensibilité individuelle et de l'exécution imaginative, étudiants et professeurs considéreront différents choix d'interprétation. A l'exception des indications *da capo*, les reprises devraient être omises aux examens.

Le Royal Conservatory of Music est très fier de ses 100 années au service de la communauté musicale internationale. Le Conservatoire souhaite à tous les usagers de la Centennial Celebration Series une grande satisfaction musicale et la joie de la découverte.

Robert K. Dodson
Principal / Directeur

Piano Repertoire Album 1
TABLE OF CONTENTS

LIST A

Menuet in F Major	4	*Mozart, L.*	4	Menuet en fa majeur
Schwäbisch	5	*Bach, J.C.F.*	5	Schwäbisch
Menuet in C Major	6	*Bach, C.P.E.*	6	Menuet en do majeur
Air in F Major	7	*Buttstedt, J.H.*	7	Air en fa majeur
Menuet in G Major	8	*Bach, J.S.*	8	Menuet en sol majeur
Air in D Minor	9	*Purcell, H.*	9	Air en ré mineur
The Fifes	10	*Dandrieu, J.F., arr.*	10	Les fifres
German Dance	11	*Beethoven, L. van*	11	Danse allemande
Allegretto in G Major	12	*Haydn, F.J.*	12	Allegretto en sol majeur
Menuet in F Major	13	*Handel, G.F.*	13	Menuet en fa majeur
Suite in C Major (complete)	14	*Hässler, J.W.*	14	Suite en do majeur (complet)
Menuet in D Minor	17	*Mozart, L., attr.*	17	Menuet en ré mineur

LIST B

The Hunt	18	*Gurlitt, C.*	18	La chasse
Early One Morning	19	**Sylvester, F., arr.*	19	Tôt le matin
The Sewing Machine	20	*Bonis, M.*	20	La machine à coudre
Rigaudon	22	*Gedike, A.*	22	Rigaudon
This Old Man	23	**Gallant, P., arr.*	23	Le vieil homme
The New Dress	24	*Stravinsky, S.*	24	La robe neuve
Battle Song, Op. 89, No. 30	25	*Kabalevsky, D.*	25	Chanson de guerre, op. 89, n° 30
Polly-Wolly-Doodle	26	**Kasemets, U., arr.*	26	Polly-Wolly-Doodle
A Happy Tale, Op. 36, No. 31	28	*Gedike, A.*	28	Un conte joyeux, op. 36, n° 31
Bears	29	**Niamath, L.*	29	Les ours
The Little Bell	30	*Garścia, J.*	30	La petite cloche
A Folk Tune	31	*Lefeld, J.*	31	Chanson folklorique
Soldier's March	32	*Shostakovich, D.*	32	Marche du soldat
Climb up on an Elephant	34	**Telfer, N., arr.*	34	Monté sur un éléphant
March (Lydian Mode)	35	**Duke D.*	35	Marche (Mode lydien)

LIST C

Invention No. 1, She's Like the Swallow	36	**Duke, D., arr.*	36	Invention n° 1, Elle est comme l'hirondelle
Invention No. 2, A Ball	37	*Garztecka, I.*	37	Invention n° 2, Une balle
Invention No. 3, On the Bridge at Avignon	38	**Gallant, P., arr.*	38	Invention n° 3, Sur le pont d'Avignon
Invention No. 4, Canon	38	*Sartorius, E.*	38	Invention n° 4, Canon
Invention No. 5, Swirling Leaves	39	**McKinnon, G.A.*	39	Invention n° 5, Tourbillon de feuilles
Invention No. 6, Dorian Invention	40	**Gallant, P.*	40	Invention n° 6, Invention dorienne
Invention No. 7, Bicinium	40	*Zoilo, A.*	40	Invention n° 7, Bicinium

Canadian composer / Compositeur canadien

MENUET IN F MAJOR / MENUET EN FA MAJEUR

LIST A

Leopold Mozart
(1719-1787)

Allegretto (M.M. ♩ = 120-132)

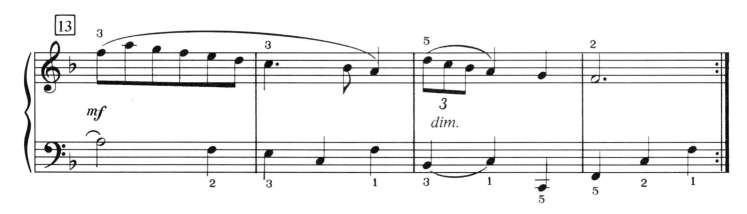

Most left-hand quarter notes may be played detached. / On peut détacher la plupart des noires de la main gauche.

Source: *Notebook for Nannerl / Album de Nannerl* (1759)

SCHWÄBISCH*

LIST A

Johann Christoph Friedrich Bach
(1732-1795)

Moderato (M.M. ♪ = 126-138)

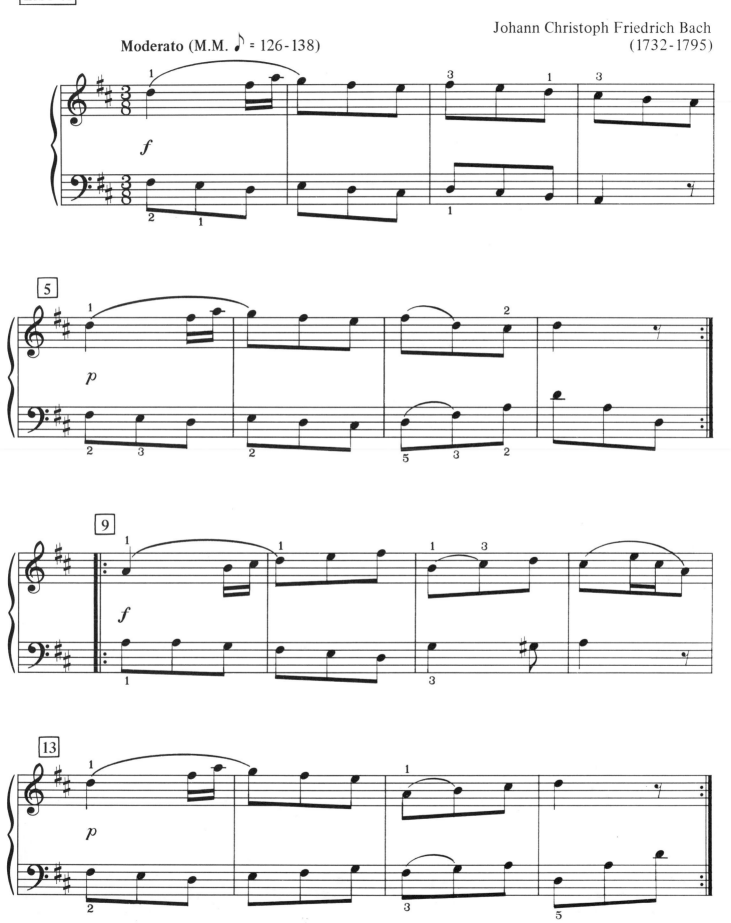

*A tune from Swabia in Germany / Un air du Swabia en Allemagne
Most eighth notes may be played staccato. / La plupart des croches peuvent être jouées staccato.

MENUET IN C MAJOR / MENUET EN DO MAJEUR

LIST A

Carl Philipp Emanuel Bach
(1714-1788)

Moderato (M.M. ♩ = 112-120)

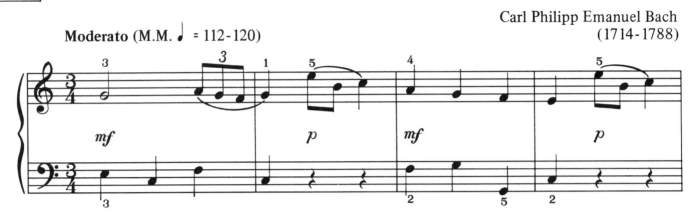

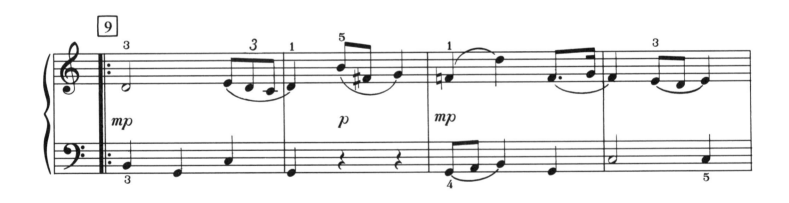

Most quarter notes may be played detached. / On peut détacher la plupart des noires.
Source: Leopold Mozart, *Notebook for Wolfgang / Album de Wolfgang* (1762)

AIR IN F MAJOR / AIR EN FA MAJEUR

LIST A

Johann Heinrich Buttstedt
(1666-1727)

Andante cantabile (M.M. ♩ = 100-108)

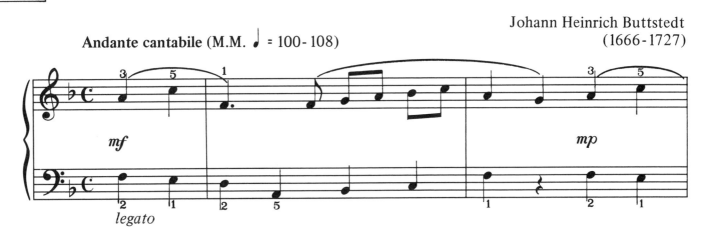

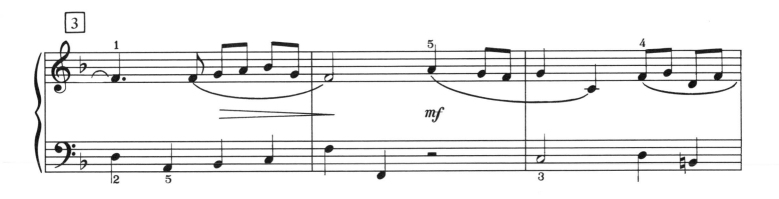

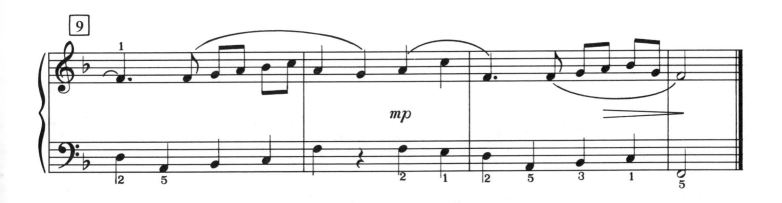

MENUET IN G MAJOR / MENUET EN SOL MAJEUR

LIST A

Johann Sebastian Bach
(1685-1750)

Most quarter notes may be played detached. / On peut détacher la plupart des noires.

Source: *Suite in G minor*, BWV 822 / *Suite en sol mineur*, BWV 822 (1700-1703)

AIR IN D MINOR / AIR EN RÉ MINEUR

LIST A

Henry Purcell
(1659-1695)

Grazioso (M.M. ♩ = 116-132)

Left-hand notes may be played slightly detached. / On peut détacher les notes de la main gauche.
Source: Instrumental Music from *The Double Dealer* / Musique instrumentale pour la pièce
The Double Dealer (1693)

THE FIFES / LES FIFRES

LIST A

Jean François Dandrieu (arr.)
(1682-1738)

Vivace (M.M. ♩ = 100-112)

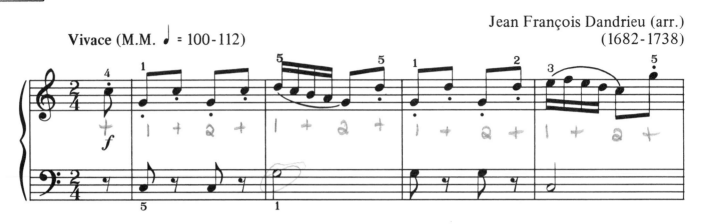

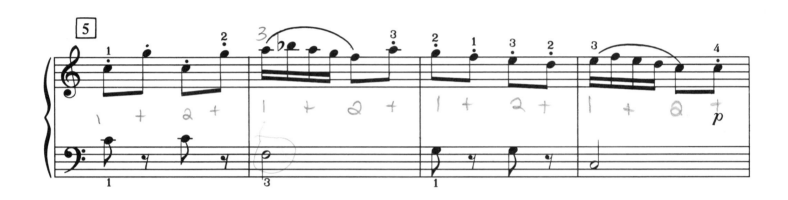

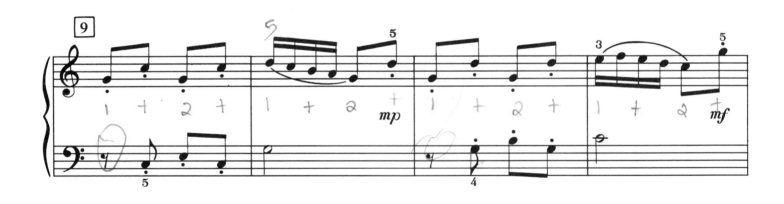

GERMAN DANCE / DANSE ALLEMANDE

LIST A

Ludwig van Beethoven
(1770-1827)

Allegretto (M.M. ♩ = 132-144)

Source: *Twelve German Dances for Orchestra*, WoO 8 / *Douze danses allemandes pour orchestre*, WoO 8 (1795)

ALLEGRETTO IN G MAJOR / ALLEGRETTO EN SOL MAJEUR

LIST A

Franz Josef Haydn
(1732-1809)

Grazioso (M.M. ♩ = 138-144)

MENUET IN F MAJOR / MENUET EN FA MAJEUR

George Frideric Handel
(1685-1759)

Most quarter notes may be played detached. / On peut détacher la plupart des noires.

SUITE IN C MAJOR / SUITE EN DO MAJEUR*
First Movement / Premier mouvement

LIST A

Johann Wilhelm Hässler
(1747-1822)

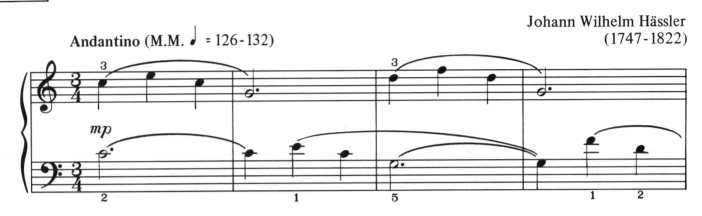

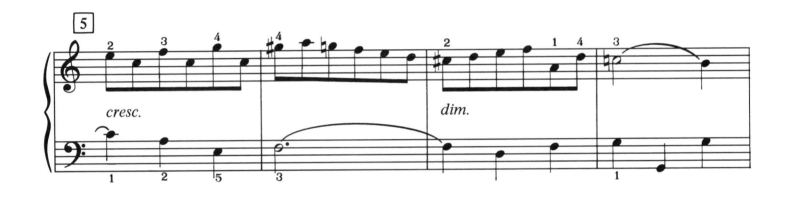

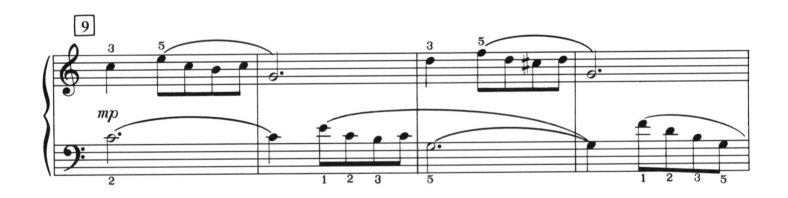

*Choose only one of the three movements for examinations. / Choisir seulement un des trois mouvements aux examens.

SUITE IN C MAJOR / SUITE EN DO MAJEUR
Second Movement / Second mouvement

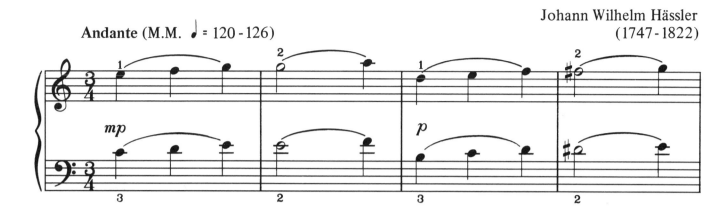

Andante (M.M. ♩ = 120 - 126)

Johann Wilhelm Hässler
(1747 - 1822)

LIST A

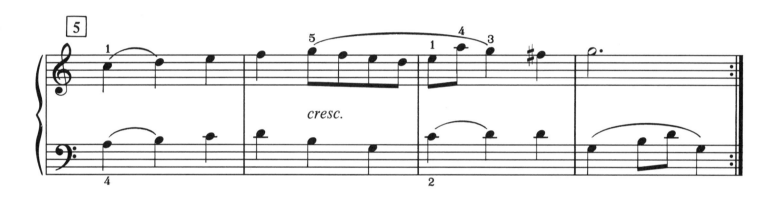

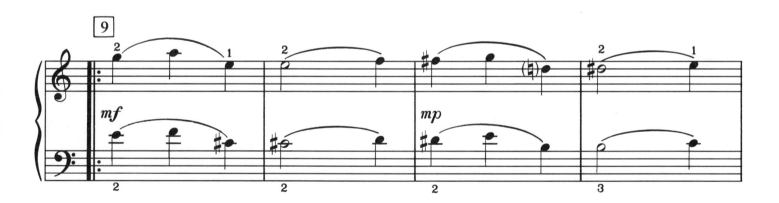

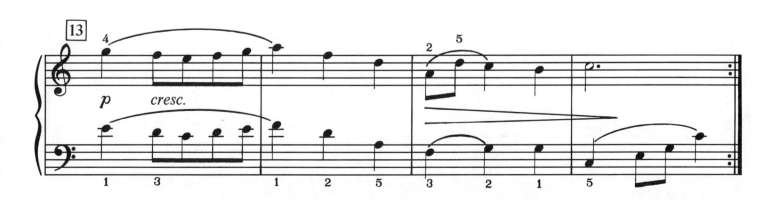

SUITE IN C MAJOR / SUITE EN DO MAJEUR
Third Movement / Troisième mouvement

Johann Wilhelm Hässler
(1747-1822)

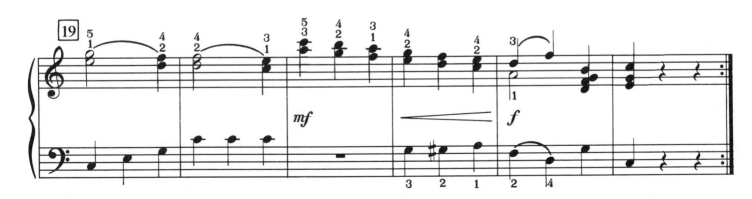

Most quarter notes may be played detached. / On peut détacher la plupart des noires.

MENUET IN D MINOR / MENUET EN RÉ MINEUR

LIST A

attributed to / attribué à
Leopold Mozart (1719-1787)

Moderato (M.M. ♩ = 120-132)

Left-hand notes may be played detached. / On peut détacher les notes de la main gauche.

Source: Leopold Mozart, *Notebook for Wolfgang / Album de Wolfgang* (1762)

THE HUNT / LA CHASSE

LIST B

Cornelius Gurlitt
(1820-1901)

EARLY ONE MORNING / TÔT LE MATIN

arr. Frederick Sylvester
(1901-1966)

LIST B

Moderato (M.M. ♩ = 80-92)

© Copyright 1968 by The Frederick Harris Music Co., Limited, Oakville, Ontario, Canada

THE SEWING MACHINE / LA MACHINE À COUDRE

LIST B

Allegro vivo (M.M. ♩ = 126-132)

Mélanie Bonis
(1858-1937)

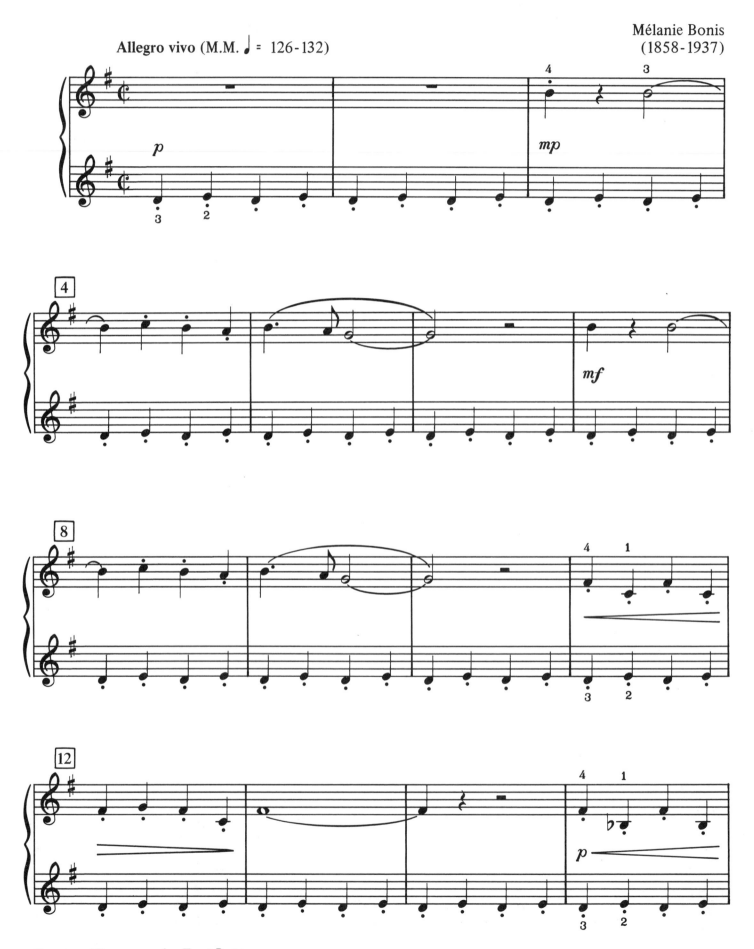

Source: *Album pour les Tout-Petits*

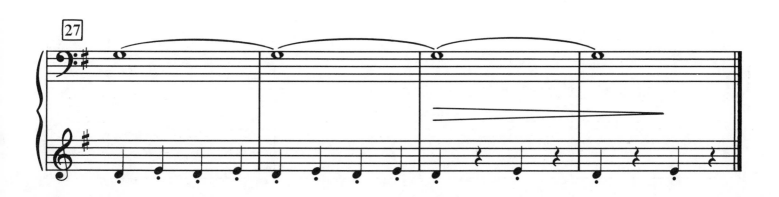

RIGAUDON

Alexander Gedike
(1877-1957)

Allegro ma non troppo (M.M. ♩ = 84-96)

THIS OLD MAN / LE VIEIL HOMME

arr. Pierre Gallant
(1950-   )

Scherzando (M.M. ♩ = 92-100)

© Copyright 1987 by Éditions Gallant Frères. Used by permission of the composer.

THE NEW DRESS / LA ROBE NEUVE

LIST B

Soulima Stravinsky
(1910-   )

Tempo di valse (M.M. ♩ = 160-176)

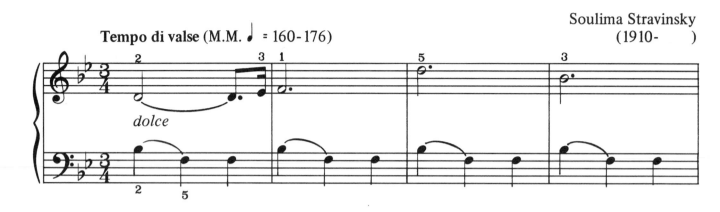

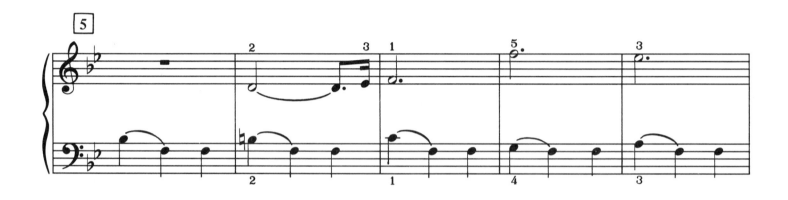

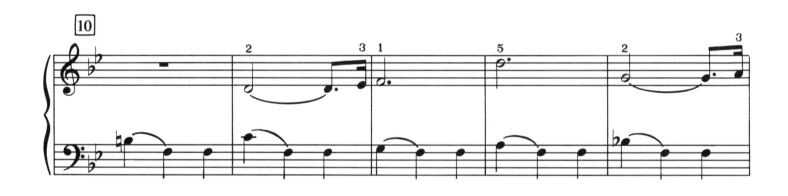

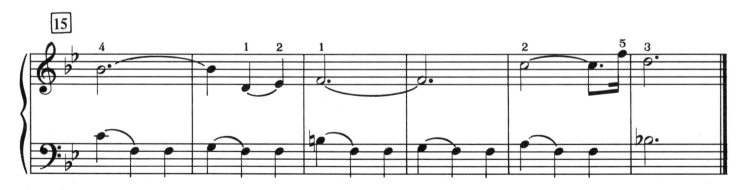

Source: *Piano Music for Children*

© Copyright 1960 by C.F. Peters Corporation, New York.
International Copyright Secured. All rights reserved. Used by permission of the publisher.

BATTLE SONG / CHANSON DE GUERRE
Op. 89, No. 30

LIST B

Dmitri Kabalevsky
(1904-1987)

Energico (M.M. ♩ = 120-132)

Source: *35 Pieces for Children / 35 Pièces pour les enfants* (1938)

POLLY - WOLLY - DOODLE

LIST B

arr. Udo Kasemets
(1919-   )

Source: *One Plus One*, Vol. 2

© Copyright 1964 by BMI Canada Limited. Copyright assigned 1969 to Berandol Music Limited.
Used by permission of Berandol Music Limited.

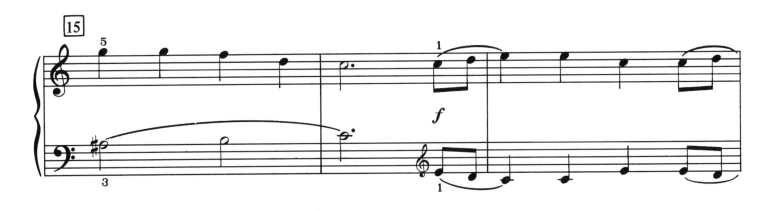

A HAPPY TALE / UN CONTE JOYEUX
Op. 36, No. 31

LIST B

Alexander Gedike
(1877-1957)

Source: *60 Simple Piano Pieces for Beginners*, Op. 36 / *60 Pièces simples pour les commençants*, op. 36

BEARS / LES OURS

Linda Niamath
(1939-   )

Source: *A Zoo for You*

© Copyright 1983 by Harmuse Publications, Oakville, Ontario, Canada

THE LITTLE BELL / LA PETITE CLOCHE

LIST B

Vivo (M.M. ♩ = 108 - 116)

Janina Garścia

© Copyright 1966 by Polskie Wydawnictwo Muzyczne, Warsaw, Poland. Used by permission.

A FOLK TUNE / CHANSON FOLKLORIQUE

LIST B

Moderato (M.M. ♩ = 96-108)

J. Lefeld

Source: *Little Frogs and Other Piano Pieces for Children*

© Copyright 1968 by Polskie Wydawnictwo Muzyczne, Warsaw, Poland. Used by permission.

SOLDIER'S MARCH / MARCHE DU SOLDAT

LIST B

Dmitri Shostakovich
(1906-1975)

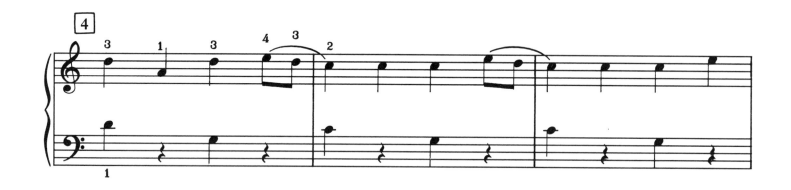

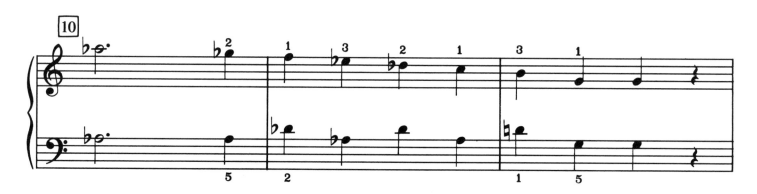

Source: *Six Children's Pieces*, Op. 69 / *Six pièces pour enfants*, op. 69 (1944-45)

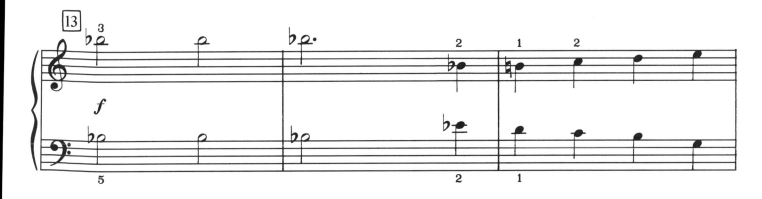

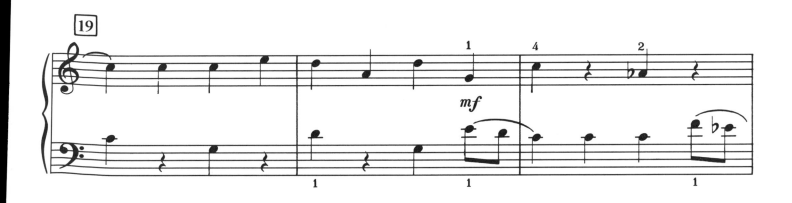

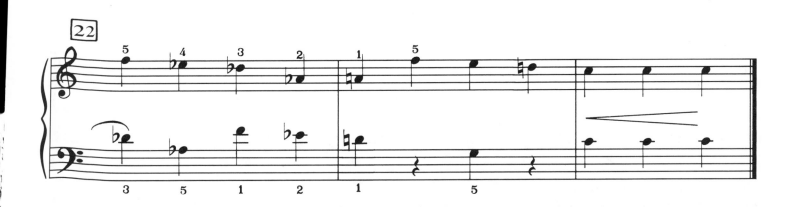

MONTÉ SUR UN ÉLÉPHANT / CLIMB UP ON AN ELEPHANT

LIST B

Awkwardly/ (M.M. ♩. = 72-88)
Maladroitement

arr. Nancy Telfer
(1950-   )

Source: *Old Tales in a New Guise*

© Copyright 1986 by The Frederick Harris Music Co., Limited, Oakville, Ontario, Canada

MARCH / MARCHE
(Lydian Mode / Mode lydien)

LIST B

David Duke
(1950-   )

Knock on wooden part of the piano.
Frappez sur le bois du piano.

Source: *Music of Our Time*, Book 1 / *Musique de notre temps*, Livre 1

© Copyright 1977 by Waterloo Music Company Limited. Reprinted by permission of Waterloo Music Company Limited.

INVENTION NO. 1
She's Like the Swallow / Elle est comme l'hirondelle

LIST C

Wistfully, moderate /
D'un air songeur et triste, modéré   (M.M. ♩. = 44 - 50)

arr. David Duke
(1950-   )

Source: *Music of Our Time,* Book 2 / *Musique de notre temps,* Livre 2
© Copyright 1977 by Waterloo Music Company Limited. Reprinted by permission of Waterloo Music Company Limited.

INVENTION NO. 2

A Ball / Une balle

LIST C

Allegro (M.M. ♩ = 160 - 176)

I. Garztecka

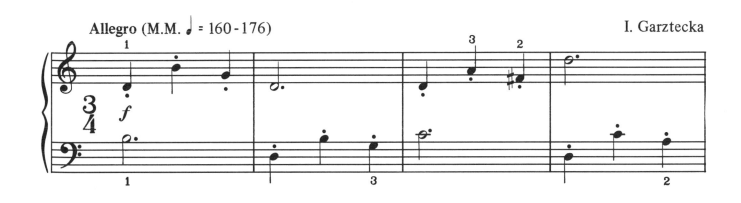

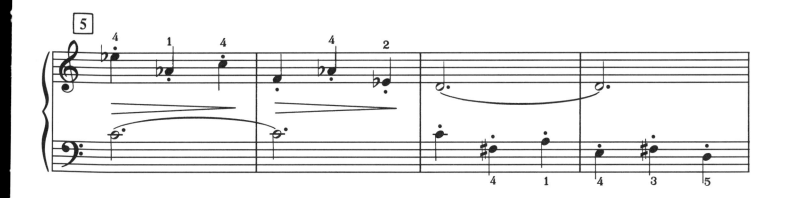

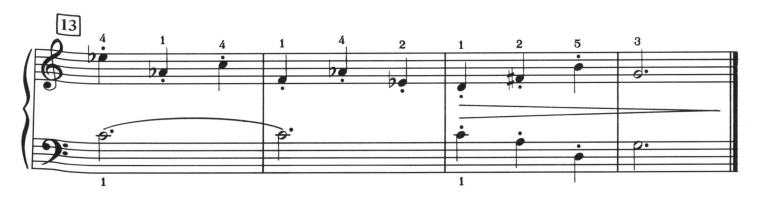

Source: *Little Frogs and Other Piano Pieces for Children*

© Copyright 1968 by Polskie Wydawnictwo Muzyczne, Warsaw, Poland. Used by permission.

INVENTION NO. 3

LIST C

Sur le pont d'Avignon / On the Bridge at Avignon

arr. Pierre Gallant
(1950-   )

© Copyright 1987 by Éditions Gallant Frères. Used by permission of the composer.

INVENTION NO. 4

LIST C

Canon

Erasmus Sartorius
(1577-1637)

INVENTION NO. 5
Swirling Leaves / Tourbillon de feuilles

LIST C

Gordon A. McKinnon
(1952-   )

Andante espressivo (M.M. ♩. = 48-54)

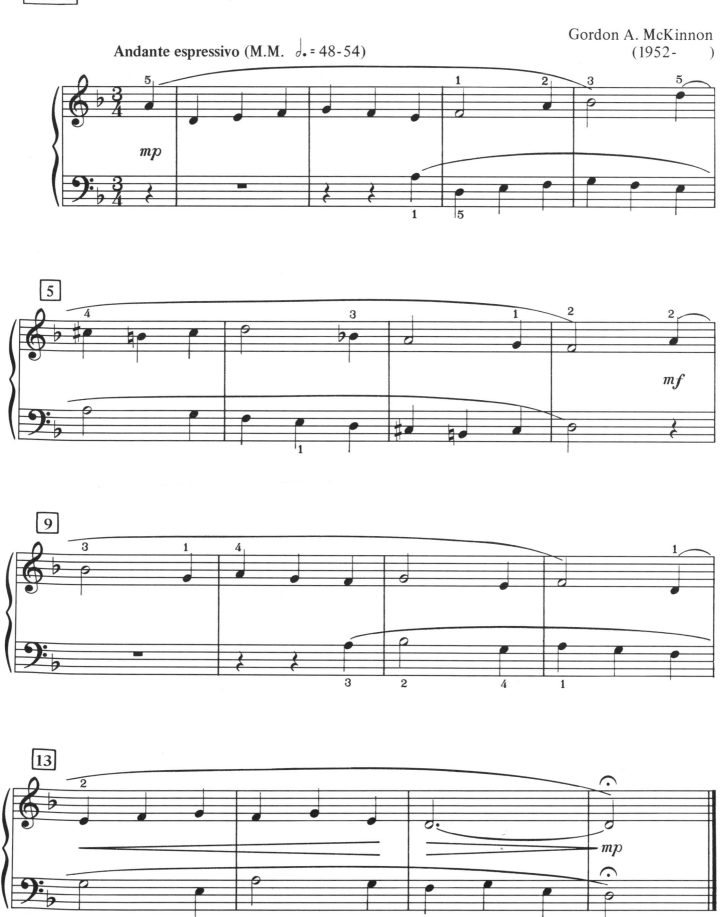

©Copyright 1987 by Gordon A. McKinnon. Used by permission of the composer.

INVENTION NO. 6
Dorian Invention / Invention dorienne

Pierre Gallant
(1950-   )

LIST C

(M.M. ♩ = 60-66)

© Copyright 1987 by Éditions Gallant Frères. Used by permission of the composer.

INVENTION NO. 7
Bicinium*

Annibale Zoilo
(1537-1592)

LIST C

(M.M. ♩ = 100-112)

*A two-part composition / Une pièce en deux parties